John Lennon Anthology.

Wise Publications
London/New York/Sydney

Exclusive distributors:

Music Sales Limited
8/9 Frith Street,
London W1V 5TZ,
England.

Music Sales Pty Limited
120 Rothschild Avenue,
Rosebery, NSW 2018,
Australia.

Art direction by Mike Bell
Book designed by Howard Brown
Compiled by Peter Evans
Typeset by Capital Setters

Photographs courtesy of:

Apple Corps. Ltd.
Apple, Dezo, Hoffman
Bob Gruen
Tony Hanley
Pictorial Press

Music Sales' complete catalogue lists thousands of
titles and is free from your local music shop, or direct from
Music Sales Limited. Please send cheque/Postal Order for £1.50 for postage to
Music Sales Limited, 8/9 Frith Street, London W1V 5TZ.

Printed in the United Kingdom by:
Redwood Books, Trowbridge, Wiltshire

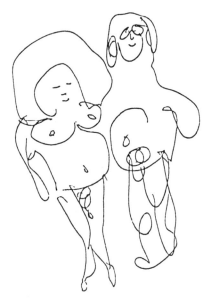

Help

Words & Music by John Lennon & Paul McCartney

Now I find   I've changed my mind,   I've o-pened up the doors._____
I know that I   just need you like   I've nev-er done be-fore._____
Help me if you

can. I'm feel-ing down _____ And I do ____ ap-pre-ci-ate ____ you be-ing 'round.____

Help me get ____ my feet back on the ground.____

Won't you please,   please____ help____ me?____

please ____ help ____ me? ____ Help   me!   Help   me! _____ Oo.

I Feel Fine

Words & Music by John Lennon & Paul McCartney

I'm so glad that she's my lit-tle girl. _____ She's so glad she's

tell-ing all the world_ That her ba - by buys her things_ you know. He buys_ her dia-mond rings_

_____ you know, She said_ so. She's in love_with me _ and I Feel_ Fine._

She's in love_with me _ and I Feel_ Fine. _____

You've Got To Hide Your Love Away

Words & Music by John Lennon

Nowhere Man

Words & Music by John Lennon & Paul McCartney

Girl

Words & Music by John Lennon & Paul McCartney

15

acts as if it's un-der-stood, She's cool ___ ooh ___ ooh ___ ooh ___

Girl. ___ oothss *(Breathe in)* Girl, ___ Girl. ___ 3. Was she

D.S. %al ✛ Coda

Coda

1. 2.

Ah, Girl. ___ oothss *(Breathe in)*

Repeat and Fade

In My Life

Words & Music by John Lennon & Paul McCartney

Norwegian Wood

Words & Music by John Lennon & Paul McCartney

I looked a-round and I no-ticed there was-n't a chair.
told her I did-n't and crawled off to sleep in the bath.

I sat on a rug bi - ding my time, drink-ing her wine,
And when I a-woke I was a - lone, this bird had flown,

We talked un - til two and then she said "It's time for bed."
So I lit a fire, Is - n't it good Nor-we - gian Wood.

To Coda ⊕

𝄋

She

D. S. al
⊕ Coda

⊕ *Coda*

Lucy In The Sky With Diamonds

Words & Music by John Lennon & Paul McCartney

Pic - ture your - self in a boat on a riv - er with
Fol - low her down to a bridge by a foun - tain where
Pic - ture your - self on a train in a sta - tion with

tan - ger - ine trees and mar - ma - lade skies
rock - ing horse peo - ple eat marsh - mal - low pies
plast - i - cine port - ers with look - ing - glass ties

Some - bo - dy calls you, you an - swer quite
Ev' - ry - one smiles as you drift past the
Sud - den - ly some - one is there at the

All You Need Is Love

Words & Music by John Lennon & Paul McCartney

sung.
saved.
shown.

No - thing you can say but you can learn how to play the game   It's
No - thing you can do but you can learn how to be you in time
No - where you can be that is - n't where ____ you're meant to be

ea - sy

All you need is love. ____

All you need is love. ____   All you need is love. ____ Love ____

To Coda

That is all ____ you need

Love   love   love

I Am The Walrus

Words & Music by John Lennon & Paul McCartney

Sit - ting on a corn-flake __ wait - ing for the van to come __
Yel - low mat - ter cus - tard __ drip - ping from a dead dog's eye __
Sem - o - li - na pil - chards __ climb - ing up the Eif - fel Tow - er __

Cor - por - a - tion tee shirt, stu - pid bloo-dy Tues-day man __ you been a naugh-ty boy - you let your face grow long __
Crab - a - lock - er fish-wife por - no - graph-ic pries-tess boy __ you been a naugh-ty girl - you let your knick-ers down __
El - e - men - t'ry pen - guin sing-ing Ha - re Krish-na man __ you should have seen them kick-ing Ed-gar Al - lan Poe __

I am the egg - man Oh they are the egg - men Oh I am the wal - rus Goo goo g'joob

To Coda

1.
Mis - ter cit - y p'lice-man sit - ting pret - ty lit - tle p'lice-men in a row __

See how they fly like Lu-cy in the sky see how _____ they run ___   I'm cry - ing ___   I'm

cry _____ ing   I'm cry - ing   I'm cry -

ing

2.

effects

Sit-ting in an En - glish gar -

den wait-ing for the sun _____   If the sun don't come ___ you get a tan from stand-ing in the Eng-lish rain -

Strawberry Fields Forever

Words & Music by John Lennon & Paul McCartney

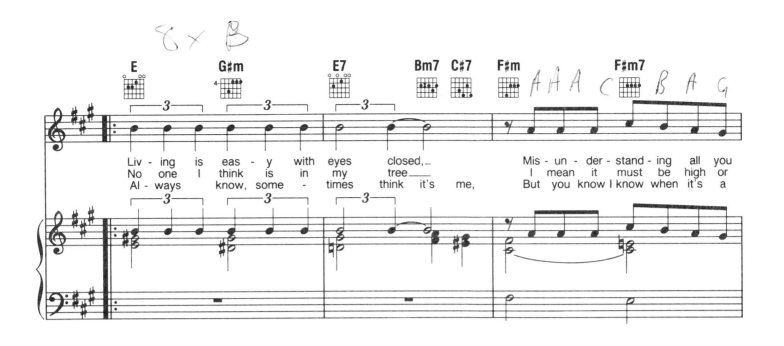

Liv - ing is eas - y with eyes closed, Mis - un - der - stand - ing all you
No one I think is in my tree I mean it must be high or
Al - ways know, some - times think it's me, But you know I know when it's a

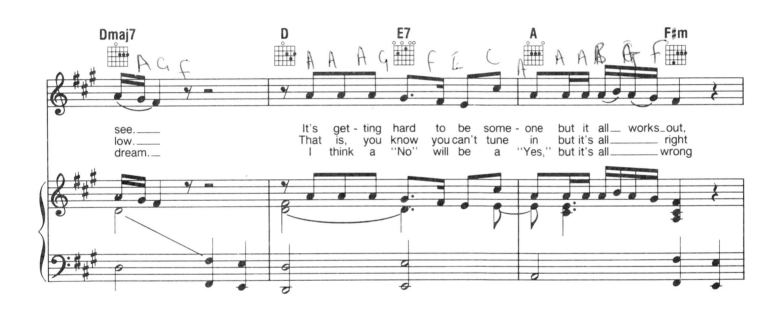

see. It's get - ting hard to be some - one but it all works out,
low. That is, you know you can't tune in but it's all right
dream. I think a "No" will be a "Yes," but it's all wrong

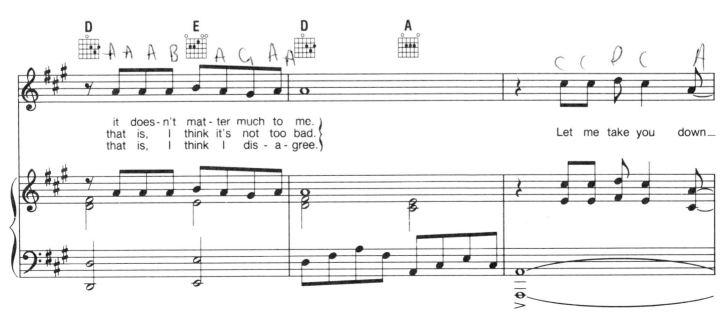

it does-n't mat - ter much to me.
that is, I think it's not too bad.
that is, I think I dis - a - gree.

Let me take you down

Julia

Words & Music by John Lennon & Paul McCartney

So I sing a song___ of love,___ , Ju - - - li -
So I sing a song___ of love,___   Ju - - - li -

a   Her hair of float - ing sky is

shim - mer - ing.   glim - mer - ing

in   the   sun. _____

Across The Universe

Words & Music by John Lennon & Paul McCartney

Sounds of laugh - ter shades of earth___ are ring - ing through my o-pen views___ in -

cit - ing and in - vit - ing me.___ Lim - it - less___ un - dy - ing love___ which

shines a - round___ me like a mil - lion suns, it calls me on and on___ a - cross___

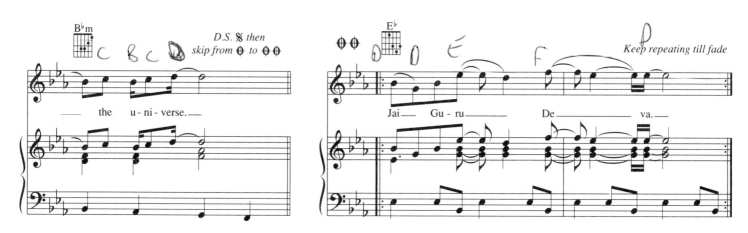

the u - ni - verse.___

Jai - Gu - ru___ De___ va.

D.S. 𝄋 then
skip from ⊕ to ⊕⊕

Keep repeating till fade

Come Together

Words & Music by John Lennon & Paul McCartney

Revolution

Words & Music by John Lennon & Paul McCartney

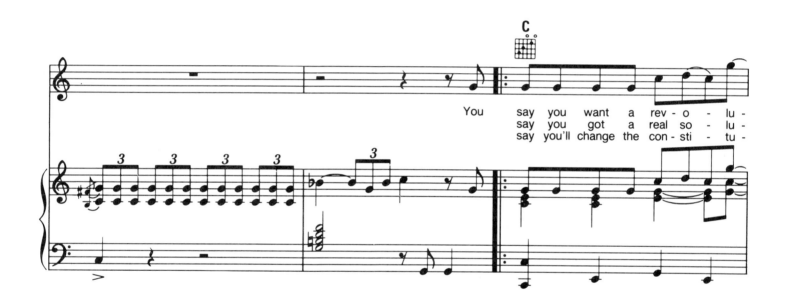

You say you want a rev-o-lu-
say you got a real so-lu-
say you'll change the con-sti-tu-

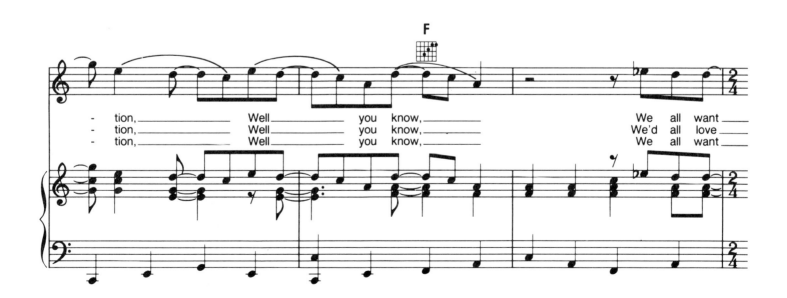

-tion,_____ Well_____ you know,_____ We all want _____
-tion,_____ Well_____ you know,_____ We'd all love _____
-tion,_____ Well_____ you know,_____ We all want _____

to change the world.
to see the plan.
to change your head.

You
You
You

tell me that it's e - vo - lu -. tion,_____ Well_____ you know,_____
ask me for a con - tri - bu - tion,_____ Well_____ you know,_____
tell me it's the in - sti - tu - tion,_____ Well_____ you know,_____

We all want_____ to change the world._____
We're all do - ing what we can._____
You better free_____ your mind in - stead.

But when you talk a - bout de - struc - tion,_____
But if you want money for people with minds that hate,_____
But if you go carry - ing pictures of Chair - man Mao,_____

Don't you know that you can count me out._____
All I can tell you is, "Brother you have to wait."_____
You ain't going to make it with any - one an - y - how._____

Don't you know it's gon-na be_____ al - right,_____

al - right,_____ al - right._____

46

The Ballad Of John And Yoko

Words & Music by John Lennon & Paul McCartney

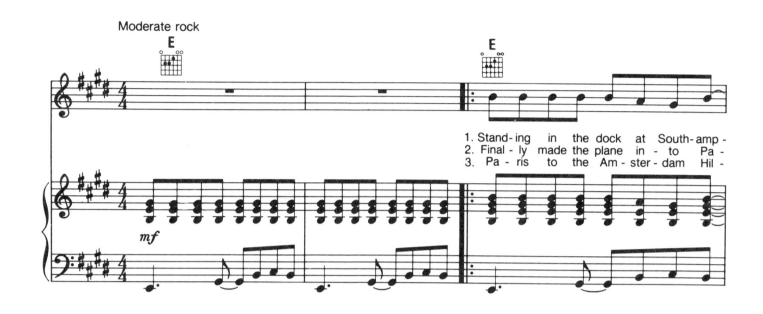

didn't e - ven give us a chance.
mar - ried in Gib - ral - ter near Spain." Christ! You know it ain't eas -

A

E

- y, you know how hard it can be.

B7

The way things are go - ing they're gon - na cru - ci - fy

E

1

2

me.

3. Drove from

eat - ing choc' - late cake in a bag.___ The news - pa - pers said,___ "She's
fif - ty a - corns tied in a sack.___ The men from the press___ said, "We

gone to his head;___ They look just like two Gu - rus in drag."___
wish you suc - cess;___ It's good to have the both of you back."___

___ { Christ! You know it ain't eas - y, you know how hard it can be.___

The way things are go - ing___

they're going to cru - ci - fy___ me.

me.   The way things are go - ing___

they're going to cru - ci - fy___ me.

Don't Let Me Down

Words & Music by John Lennon & Paul McCartney

Give Peace A Chance

Words & Music by John Lennon & Paul McCartney

Ev - 'ry - bod - y's talk - ing a - bout
Ev - 'ry - bod - y's talk - ing a - bout
Ev - 'ry - bod - y's talk - ing a - bout
Ev - 'ry - bod - y's talk - ing a - bout

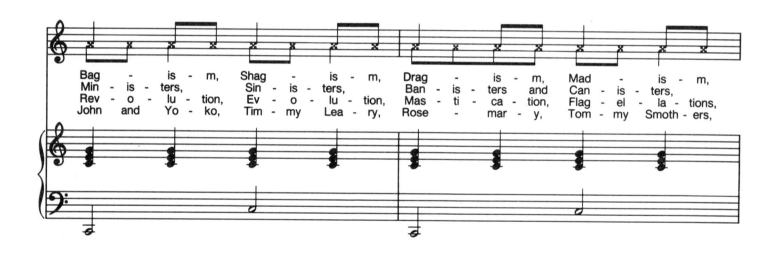

Bag - is - m, Shag - is - m, Drag - is - m, Mad - is - m,
Min - is - ters, Sin - is - ters, Ban - is - ters and Can - is - ters,
Rev - o - lu - tion, Ev - o - lu - tion, Mas - ti - ca - tion, Flag - el - la - tions,
John and Yo - ko, Tim - my Lea - ry, Rose - mary, Tom - my Smoth - ers,

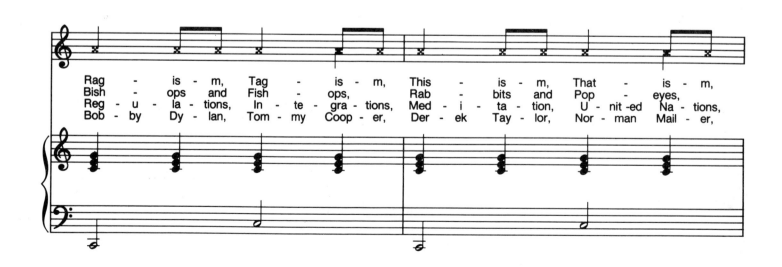

Rag - is - m, Tag - is - m, This - is - m, That - is - m,
Bish - ops and Fish - ops, Rab - bits and Pop - eyes,
Reg - u - la - tions, In - te - gra - tions, Med - i - ta - tion, U - nit -ed Na - tions,
Bob - by Dy - lan, Tom - my Coop - er, Der - ek Tay - lor, Nor - man Mail - er,

Is - n't it the most?
Bye- bye   Bye-byes.
Con- grad - u - la - tions.
Al - len Gins-berg, Ha - re Krish-na Ha - re, Ha - re Krish - na.

All   we___ are

say   -   ing_____   is   give peace___ a

chance._____   All   we___ are

say   -   ing_____   is   give peace___ a

chance.

C'-mon

Let me tell you now. Oh let's stick to it. All we___ are

say - ing___ is give peace_ a

chance.

All we___ are

Repeat ad lib. and Fade

I Want You (She's So Heavy)

Words & Music by John Lennon & Paul McCartney

Cold Turkey

Words & Music by John Lennon

I wish I was a ba - by
One thing I'm sure — of
I pro-mise you an - y - thing —

I wish I was dead —
I'm in at the deep — freeze
get me out of this hell —

D7   Am7 D7 Am   (tacet)   D7   Am7 D7 Am   (tacet)

Cold Tur - key _____   has   got   me _____

Am   C   D

To Coda

_____ on the run _____   (Ah —)   (Ah

(tacet--------------------) A7   D   Am

1   2

My _____   Ah _____

D6(no 3rd)   D6(no 3rd)   D7   Am7 D7 Am   D7   Am7 D7 Am

Oh ———————— Oo ——————————— Oh ——

D7 Am7 D7 Am   D7   Am7 D7 Am   D7   Am7 D7 Am   D7   Am7 D7 Am   D7   Am7 D7 Am

——— Cold Tur - key ————————— has got me ——————— on the run

D7 Am7 D7 Am   C   D   (tacet————————

D.℀ al Coda

————A7   D   Am   D6(no 3rd)

⊕ CODA

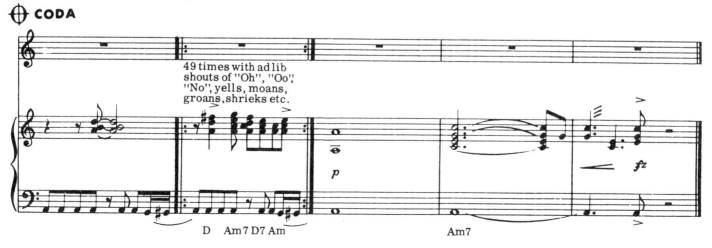

49 times with ad lib
shouts of "Oh", "Oo",
"No", yells, moans,
groans, shrieks etc.

D Am7 D7 Am   Am7

Power To The People

Words & Music by John Lennon

——ple.　　Pow-er　to　the　peo-ple right on. ——　　　　　　　You

2. A mil-lion
3. I gon-na

D　　　Em　D　D　　　Cmaj7　　　D

say you want a　rev-o-lu————tion,　　we'd bet-ter get　　on　　right　a-way—
work-ers work——in' for no——thing,　you bet-ter give them what they real-ly own—
ask　you com——rades and bro——thers,　how do you treat your old wo-man back home—

Em

——　　Well let's get　on　your feet, ——　　　　end　of　the street,— sing-ing
——　　We got-ta　put you　down— when we come in-to ——　town, — sing-ing
——　　She's got-ta　be her-self — so she can give us —— help, — sing-ing
　　　　　　　　　　　　　　　　　　　　　　　　　　　　　Oh well —

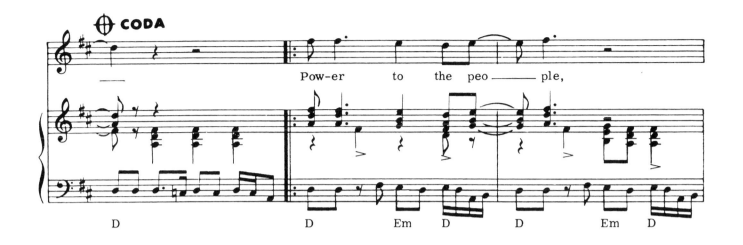

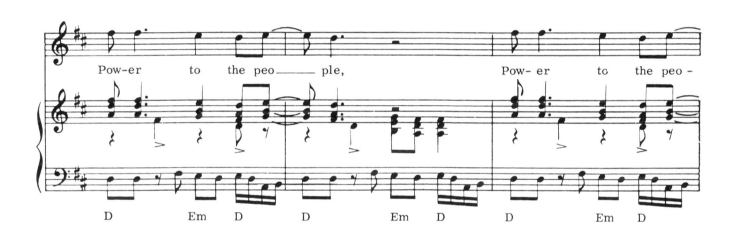

Jealous Guy

Words & Music by John Lennon

Moderately Slow

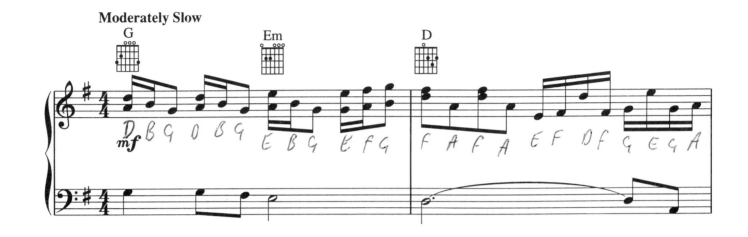

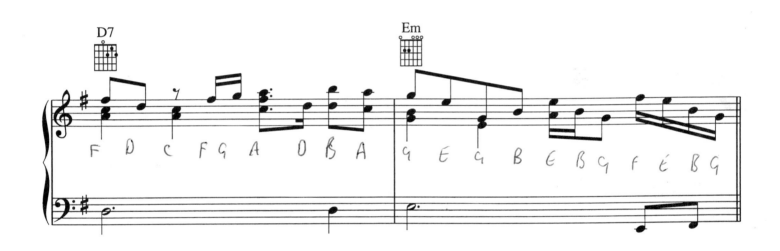

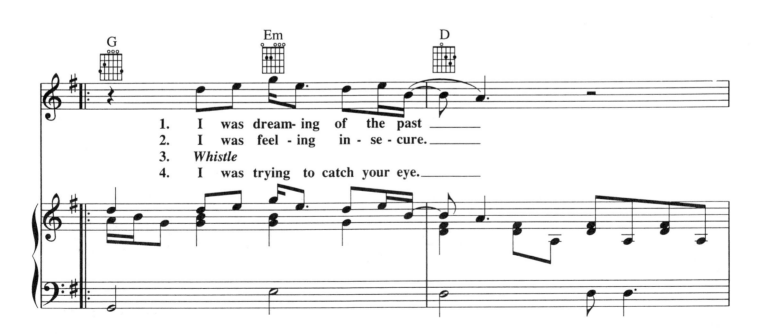

1. I was dream-ing of the past ____
2. I was feel-ing in-se-cure. ____
3. *Whistle*
4. I was trying to catch your eye. ____

I did - n't mean___ to hurt ___ you. _____

I'm sor - ry that ___ I made _____ you cry. Oh, no.

I did - n't want___ to hurt _____ you.

I'm just __ a jea-lous guy.
(2,3) guy. _____

you.   I'm just __ a jea-lous guy, _____ watch out.

I'm just __ a jea-lous guy, look out __ babe. __ I'm just __ a jea-lous guy. _____

Working Class Hero

Words & Music by John Lennon

soon as you're born _____ they make you feel small _____

by giv-ing you no time in-stead of it all. _____

Till the pain is so big you feel no-thing at all.

2. They hurt you at home and they hit you at school
   They hate you if you're clever and they despise a fool
   Till you're so fucking crazy you can't follow their rules
   (Chorus)

3. When they've tortured and scared you for 20 odd years
   Then they expect you to pick a career
   When you can't really function you're so full of fear
   (Chorus)

4. Keep you doped with religion and sex and t.v.
   And you think you're so clever and classless and free
   But you're still fucking peasants as far as I can see
   (Chorus)

5. There'e room at the top they are telling you still
   But first you must learn how to smile as you kill
   If you want to be like the folks on the hill
   (Chorus)

74

Oh Yoko

Words & Music by John Lennon

Oh Yo___ko.

Db   Ab7   Db   Gb Db

Oh Yo___ko.   My

Db   Ab7   Bbm   Db

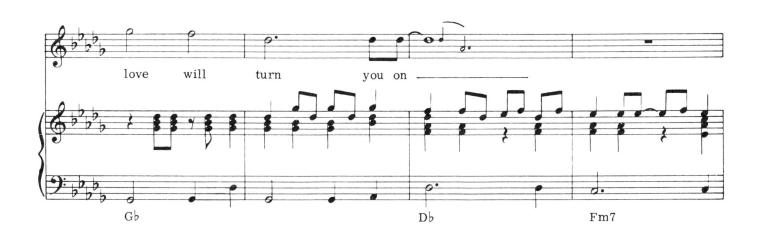

love will turn you on ___

Gb   Db   Fm7

1.3.   **2.4.**

My love ___

Bbm   Bbm   Gb

will _____ turn _____

you _____ on.

Db

Fm7   Bbm   Bbm

Repeat till fade with ad lib harmonica accomp.

Oh   Yo _____ ko. _____

Db   Ab7   Db   Gb   Db

How

Words & Music by John Lennon

Slowly (♩=80)

How can I ___ go for-ward when I don't know which way I'm fac - ing ___
How can I ___ have feel-ing when I don't know if it's a feel - ing ___
How can I ___ give love when I don't know what it is I'm giv - ing ___
How can we ___ go for-ward when we don't know which way we're fac - ing ___

G

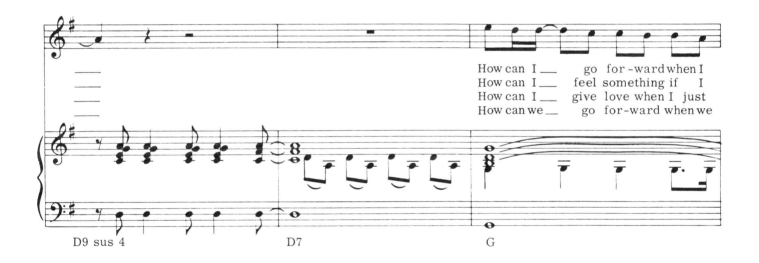

How can I ___ go for-ward when I
How can I ___ feel something if I
How can I ___ give love when I just
How can we ___ go for-ward when we

D9 sus 4   D7   G

don't know which way to turn ___
just don't know how to feel ___
don't know how to give ___
don't know which way to turn ___

D7sus4

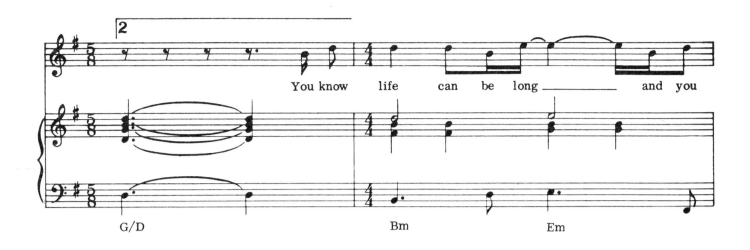

You know life can be long _____ and you

got to be __ so strong _____ and the world __ is so tough __

some - times I feel I've had e - nough

D.C. (twice) **al Coda**

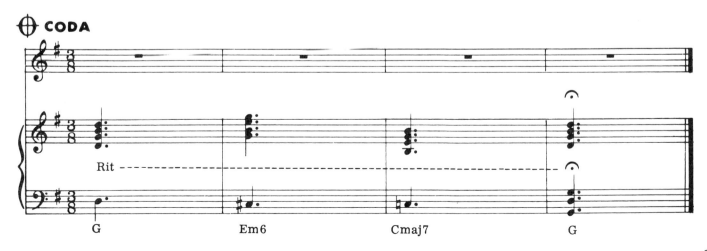

Sunday Bloody Sunday

Words & Music by John Lennon & Yoko Ono

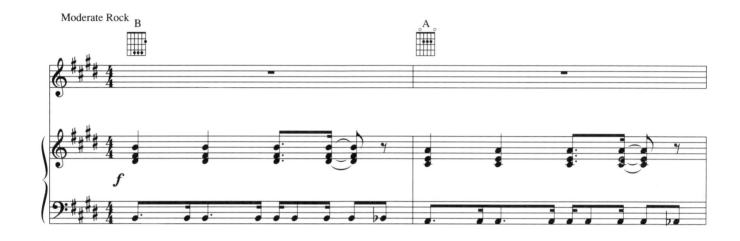

1. Well, it was

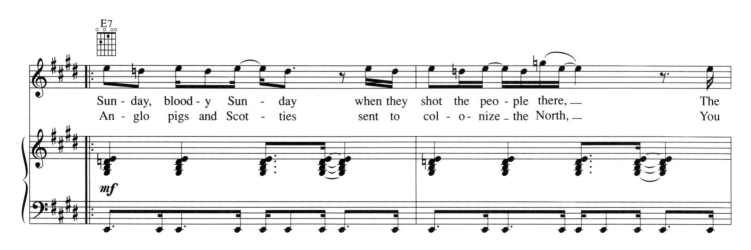

Sun - day, blood - y Sun - day   when they shot the peo - ple there, —   The
An - glo pigs and Scot - ties   sent to col - o - nize — the North, —   You

cries of thir - teen mar - tyrs filled the Free ____ Der - ry air. ____ Is there
wave your blood - y un - ion jacks and you know what it's worth. ____ How

G6

an - y - one ____ a - mongst you dare to blame it on the kids? ____ Not a
dare you hold ____ to ran - som a peo - ple proud and free, ____ Keep

A7 Tacet

sol - dier boy was bleed - ing when they nailed the cof - fin lids! ____
Ire - land for the I - rish, put the Eng - lish back to sea! ____

B   A   G

Sun - day, blood - y Sun - day, Blood - y Sun - day's the

f

Happy Xmas (War Is Over)

Words & Music by John Lennon & Yoko Ono

Whatever Gets You Through The Night

Words & Music by John Lennon

right.___
right.___
right.___

Don't need a sword to cut thru' flow-ers, ___
Don't need a watch to waste your time, _____
Don't need a gun to blow your mind, _____

Oh no___ oh no___

What-ev-er gets you thru' your

Hold me dar - lin', come on lis - ten to__ me, I won't do__ you no

harm; Trust me dar - lin', come on lis - ten to__ me, come on lis - ten to__ me, come on

lis - ten,__ lis - ten.__

Solo

D.S. (no repeat) fade on last
Tacet   *Instrumental section*

What - ev - er gets you to the

Fade last time _ _ _ _ _ _ _ _ _ _ _ _ _ _ *

C   _ G   Tacet _ _ _ _ _ _ _ _ _ *

Woman

Words & Music by John Lennon

thank - ful - ness__   for show-ing me   the   mean - ing of suc -
keep us a - part.__   Af - ter all,   it is   writ - ten in the

cess. _____
stars. _____   Ooh, _____

____ well, well.   Doo doo doo   doo doo.   Ooh, _____

____ well, well.   Doo doo doo   doo doo.   doo doo.

Wom-an, please let me ex - plain._

I nev-er meant to cause you sor-row or pain._ So let me tell you a -

gain and a - gain and a - gain:_____ I

Repeat and fade

love _____ you, yeah, yeah, now and for - ev-er. I

Watching The Wheels

Words & Music by John Lennon

Peo-ple say I'm cra - zy
Peo-ple say I'm la - zy,
Peo-ple ask-ing ques - tions,

do-in' what I'm do - in'.___
dream-in' my life___ a - way.___
lost in con - fu - sion.___

When I say that I'm___ O K,___ well they look at me kind - a strange:___
tell 'em that I'm do - in' fine___ watch-ing shad - ows on___ the wall,___
shake their heads and they look at me___ as if I've lost___ my mind.___

"Sure - ly you're___ not hap - py now___ you no
"Don't you miss___ the big___ time, boy?___ You're no
I tell them there's___ no hur - ry. I'm___ just

long - er play___ the game."___
long - er on___ the ball."___
sit - ting here do - ing time.___

I'm Losing You

Words & Music by John Lennon

Here in the val - ley of in - de - ci - sion, I don't know_ _ what to do. I feel you slip-ping a -way. I feel you slip-ping a -way. _____

I'm los - ing you._

I'm los - ing you._

103

(Just Like) Starting Over

Words & Music by John Lennon

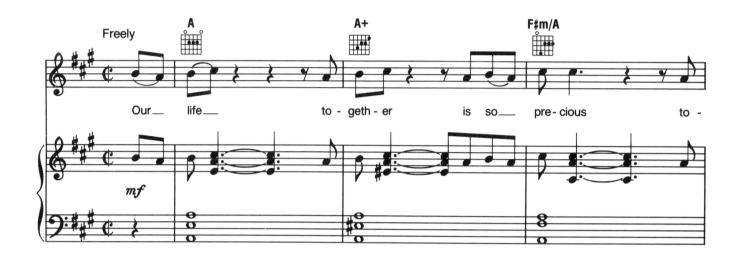

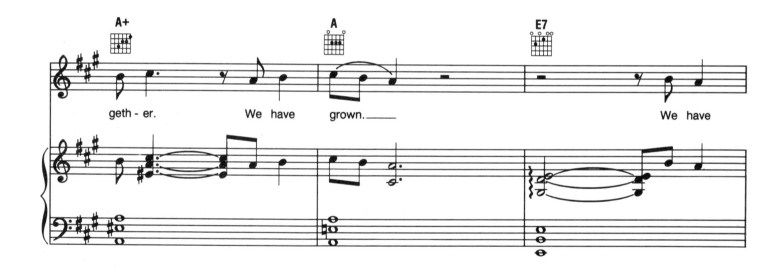

trip some-where far, far a-way,___ We'll be to-

geth - er all a - lone_____ a - gain, like we

used to___ in the ear - ly days.___ Well, well,

dar - lin'. It's Our___

D.S. (lyric 1) al Coda

CODA

love

is still spe - cial,

let's take___ a chance and___ fly a -

way_____ some - where._____

Repeat (vocal ad lib.) and Fade

Beautiful Boys

Words & Music by Yoko Ono

I'm Your Angel

Words & Music by Yoko Ono

Yes, I'm your an - gel. I'll give you ev - 'ry-thing
pret - ty. You're so diz - zy. And we're so

in my mag - ic pow - er. So, make a wish and I'll let it
hap - py ev - 'ry day. Let's make a wish and let it

come   true for you,   tra la la la la.   You're my
come   true for us,   tra la la la la.   I'm in your

fair - y.   You give me ev-'ry-thing   I   ev - er want-ed from
pock - et.   You're in my lock - et.   And we're so luck-y   in ev - 'ry

life.   Have I made a   wish,   and is that   why   I have
way.   We make a   wish,   and let it   come   true for

you,   tra la la la la?   We be-lieve in pump-kins   that turn in-to
us,   tra la la la la.   We be-lieve in hous - es   built in the

prin-cess and frogs that turn in-to prince. We be
sky and love that lifts us high. We be-

lieve in moons that smile to us___ when we hur-ry home ___ be-fore the
lieve in the sun that looks o - ver our shoul-ders and brings our shad ___ ows to-

mid-night strikes, tra la la la la. Yes, I'm so tra la la la la. Yes, our
geth - er,

hearts are one. Our bod-ies, too. And it's so good___

ev-'ry time __ we make a wish and let it come true for you

too, tra la la la la. Hap-py birth-day, my love. I'm your

an-gel. I'll give you ev-'ry-thing __ in my mag-ic pow-er. So make a

wish, and I'll let it come true for you, tra la la la la la. __

Love

Words & Music by John Lennon

Love is feel - ing,
Love is reach - ing,
Love is liv - ing,

feel - ing Love.
reach - ing Love.
liv - ing Love.

Love is want - ing
Love is ask - ing
Love is need - ing

to be loved.
to be loved.
to be loved.

Love is touch,

Love is you,

you and me,

Love is know-

121

D.S. ℅ al Coda ⊕

- ing___ we can be;___ Love is free,___

Coda
⊕

D

No chords

pp

Imagine

Words & Music by John Lennon

Im - ag - ine all the peo -
Im - ag - ine all the peo -

ple living life in peace.
ple sharing all the world.

You you may say I'm a

dream - er. But I'm not the on - ly one.

126